A CHAIR FULL OF HEART

written by Vicky Cavin
illustrated by Sally R. Simmer

HARA
PUBLISHING GROUP

Published by
Hara Publishing
P.O. Box 19732
Seattle, WA 98109

ISBN: 1-883697-25-5
Library of Congress Number: 97-078247

Illustration: Sally R. Simmer
Cover Design: Shael Anderson
Desktop Publishing: Shael Anderson

For my mother, Glenna,
and my daughter, Halli.

Through love
may our rivers
become streams.

Mama's Hands

© Sally R. Simmer '87

Mama's hands were seasoned,
By years of sunlight and bleach,
Torn by thorns and
Bruised and worn,
Yet still within my reach.

Her fingers held the needles,
But her heart knit every row,
Through the years, and
Tears and fears,
Her sweaters helped me grow.

I Remember . . .

I was eight when I gave the heart to Mama. I made it out of torn paper fitted together and glued to cardboard. On the heart I wrote my first rhyme.

I remember watching the lines in her face soften as she sat in the overstuffed chair to open the envelope. As she read the words, my heart pounded.

It read:

To Mom,
If things change
As time goes by
And we are apart,
Hold still, and feel
My love for you,
And my
forever heart.
Love,
Your Daughter

She smiled and told me she'd treasure it forever. Then she stared straight through my eyes into my heart. "You are a writer," she whispered. She had a way of making me believe it. From that moment on, words bounced from my head to my hands, revealing themselves on paper, like shy new friends.

Mama always had a place for everything. "Organization is the key," she'd say. I figured she'd put my heart away in just the right place, because after a week, it disappeared. I knew it must be the beginning of a new collection.

Mama claimed her collecting habit came from growing up in a family of nine during The Great Depression, when there were plenty of beans and little else. As a girl, she lined her pockets with unusual rocks, and later, the rooms of our house with treasures from the past.

There were great-great-grandmother's quilts, lamps of brass, French clocks, and delicate hand-painted dishes. Curly-haired dolls with porcelain faces, glass-beaded bags and hand-blown vases. Cherry-wood rockers and caned-oak chairs, umbrellas of old.

Of all of these, I loved the overstuffed chair the best. It wasn't fancy, or valuable, but it was where I knew I could find Mother when she finally sat down to correct papers from her school teaching job, or cut scraps of wool to make hand-braided rugs. Or embroider pillow cases, or knit sweaters.

We'd have some great talks then. Sometimes I'd bring her bowls of popcorn, or potato soup, and she'd tell me funny stories about the old days and hard times. Like when she tried to dry her baby brother's only shoes by baking them in the oven.

S.R. SIMMER '97"

Sometimes anger passed between Mama and me like a cold that wouldn't leave, bringing chills and raising temperatures. Maybe it was her wanting me to be "just so." Mama disliked unmade beds, being late to anything and "half-way-done" jobs. She'd say, "If you're going to do it, do it right, or not at all."

At fourteen, my beehive hairdo and 45's were more important than unmade beds and half-way-done jobs. I stared at the stranger in the chair, and silently back-talked her every word.

As I grew taller, amd brave enough to make my own path, the years brought changes that weren't easy to understand. Mama and I faced each other from opposite banks, with a raging river between.

In time the river dwindled into a stream. A stream so tiny in places, Mama and I could reach each other; and, hand in hand, walk through our differences.

Mama soon taught me to yearn for second-hand stores and garage sales, and we began to share recipes and lunches in off-beat cafes. And when she held her baby granddaughter for the first time, Mama showed me how deep her love went.

I could see it in her dimples.

As Christmases and birthdays passed year after year into photo albums, Mama's hair grayed and her hands, seasoned by the sun, became freckled in brown. She'd call each evening just to ask, "How was your day?" When I dropped her back home after a lunch out, she'd ask, "Would you come in and visit a while longer?"

©Sally R. Jimmer 97

One morning she invited me for coffee and a roll. Looking straight through my eyes, all the way to my heart, she simply said, "I have cancer. I'm going to fight it because as long as there's life, there's hope."

We cried deeply that morning, with arms tightly holding each other. Not even a stream between us.

Mother's bravery was amazing to some, but it shouldn't have been surprising. Not for a person who believed, "If you're going to do it, do it right, or don't do it at all."

As she fought to keep the cancer from spreading, she lost her hair, her energy, and the desire for food. I'd find her in the chair, wrapped in a blanket. No knitting needles or yarn. No quilting threads. Just plenty of determination. "I think it's time for me to get a wig," she whispered. "Could you pick me up tomorrow?"

Wearing a turban around her balding head, she greeted me the next morning at the back door. Standing in the sunlight, she never seemed more beautiful. We sipped tea. Then drove to find the wig lady.

One chilly morning in December I found Mama unable to breathe. At the hospital we learned that a tumor had filled her lungs with fluid. While Santa visited her room, and carolers softly sang in the hall of the oncology ward, a tiny tree with lights cast a glow on flowers and plants that filled her room. After all the years of festive holiday dinners, Christmas came down to one simple gathering in room 824.

Days later we held hands and embraced the stillness. It seemed as though the last few grains of sand in her hourglass were passing silently into the morning. "You're one in a million," Mama whispered. Looking straight through her eyes and into her heart, I said, "I love you, Mom."

After a coma, she died.

© Sally R. Summer 97

When the flowers and tears had dried and friends and cards had long stopped coming, I stared through the doorway into the emptiness of nooks and crannies, once the home of her beloved collections.

© Sally R Simmer 97'

Everything I had touched had meant a decision—the letters from World War II, the flo-blue dishes, the hand-knit sweaters. The big truck would be coming back any moment for one last load.

I felt oceans move from my toes, through my heart, to my throat. Oceans once deep and dark and far away, now too close. I let go the tears and walked towards the over-stuffed chair. Weeping softly, I pulled a corner of worn cardboard, wedged between the cushion and springs. It was wrinkled and faded, but after all those years, I had found my heart.

I sat slowly down in the chair where I could always find Mama. I sat very still and read my first rhyme.

To Mom,
If things change
As time goes by
And we are apart,
Hold still, and feel
My love for you,
And my forever heart.
Love,
Your Daughter

Special thanks:

to Grady and Halli Cavin, Jerry, Jay and Jennine Simmer,
Dorthy Didier, Mel and Sue Shaw, Mel's Floral and Gift,
Eli Martin Christianson, Joni Titus, Anne McKeon,
Sylvia Lenz, Carolyn Sutherland, Holy Family Hospital,
Jay and Jackie Runkel, Marcie Oster,
Greg and Teresa Riddle, and
the American Cancer Society.